Music for
Common Worship
Holy Communion

A treasury of settings to enhance the new services

We hope you enjoy the music in this book. Further copies are available
from your local music shop or Christian bookshop.

In case of difficulty, please contact the publisher direct by writing to:

The Sales Department
KEVIN MAYHEW LTD
Buxhall
Stowmarket
Suffolk IP14 3BW

Phone 01449 737978
Fax 01449 737834
E-mail info@kevinmayhewltd.com

Please ask for our complete catalogue of outstanding Church Music.

The Publishers wish to express their gratitude to The Archbishops' Council of the Church of
England, Church House, Great Smith Street, London SW1P 3NZ, for permission to use
extracts from *Common Worship: Services and Prayers for the Church of England.*

The extracts from *Common Worship: Services and Prayers for the Church of England,*
are copyright © The Archbishops' Council, 2000 and are reproduced by permission.
Extracts (and adapted extracts) from *The Book of Common Prayer,* the rights in which
are vested in the Crown, are reproduced by permission of the
Crown's Patentee,Cambridge University Press.

First published in Great Britain in 2000 by Kevin Mayhew Ltd.

© Copyright 2000 Kevin Mayhew Ltd.

ISBN 1 84003 621 4
ISMN M 57004 750 5
Catalogue No: 1400256

0 1 2 3 4 5 6 7 8 9

Cover design by Jonathan Stroulger

Music editor and setter: Donald Thomson
Proof reader: Sally Gough

Printed and bound in Great Britain

Contents

FOREWORD

Common Worship, the new services for the Anglican Church, contains a good number of new texts which may be sung, and it is these that are set to music in this book.

We have asked our composers to provide music that is attractive and accessible to both congregation and choir.

Everything here is suitable for congregational unison singing but much of it may also be sung in harmony by the choir as well. The choice is given at the beginning of each piece.

We hope that this modest collection will do its part in launching *Common Worship* into the churches who in turn will benefit from this fine new set of services.

The Publisher

THE PREPARATION

The Commandments

Andrew Moore

7

President **All** *(Harmony)*

You shall not covet anything which belongs to your neigh - bour. A - men. Lord, have

mer - cy on us and write all these your laws in our hearts.

OR Rosalie Bonighton

All *(Harmony)*

Lord, have mer-cy up - on us, and in-cline our hearts to keep this law.

Lord, have mer - cy,

Final Response

All *(Harmony)*

Lord, have mer-cy up - on us, and write all these your laws in our hearts.

Lord, have mer - cy,

OR
Traditional Language Setting

Betty Roe

Lord, have mer-cy up-on us, and in-cline our hearts to keep this law.

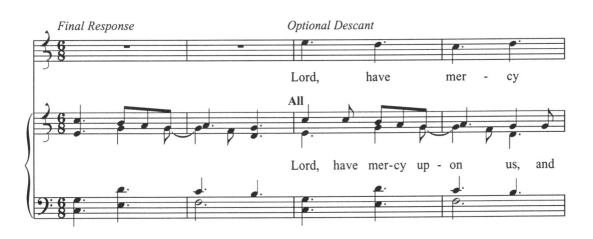

Final Response

Optional Descant

Lord, have mer-cy

Lord, have mer-cy up-on us, and

write all these thy laws in our hearts, we be-seech thee.

write all these thy laws in our hearts, we be-seech thee.

Summary of the Law

Andrew Moore

A - men. Lord, have mer - cy.

Prayers of Penitence

Andrew Moore

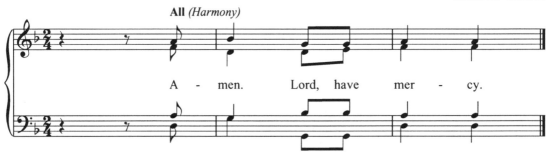

A - men. Lord, have mer - cy.

OR

Traditional Language Setting

Betty Roe

Lord, have mer-cy up - on us, and

write all these thy laws in our hearts, we be - seech thee.

The Greeting

Andrew Moore

The Lord be with you and al - so with you.

OR

Rosalie Bonighton

Grace, mer - cy and peace from God our Fa - ther and the

Lord Je - sus Christ be with you and al - so with you.

From Easter Day to Pentecost this acclamation follows:

Rosalie Bonighton

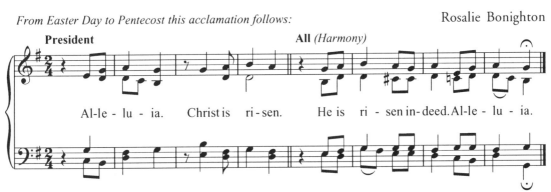

Al-le - lu - ia. Christ is ri - sen. He is ri - sen in - deed. Al-le - lu - ia.

Confessions

Andrew Moore

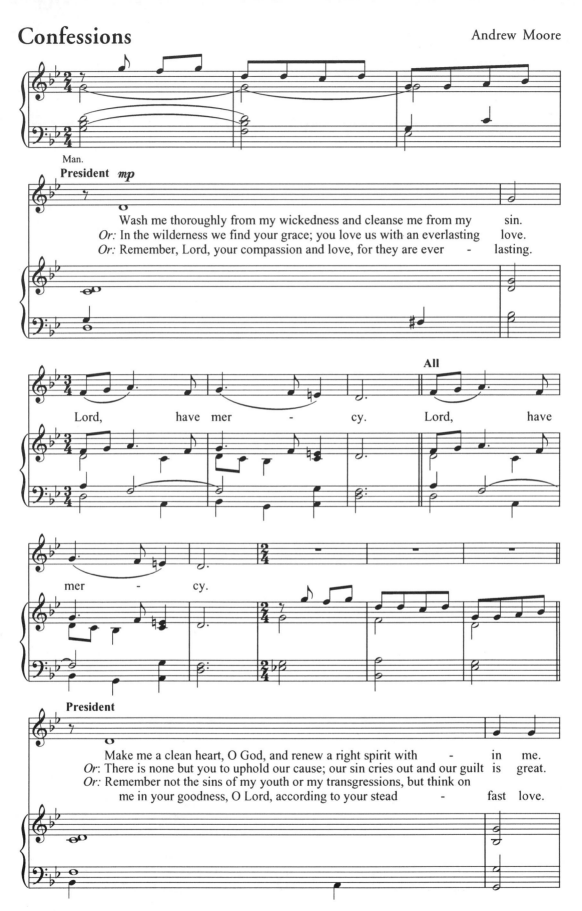

President *mp*

Wash me thoroughly from my wickedness and cleanse me from my sin.
Or: In the wilderness we find your grace; you love us with an everlasting love.
Or: Remember, Lord, your compassion and love, for they are ever - lasting.

All

Lord, have mer - cy. Lord, have mer - cy.

President

Make me a clean heart, O God, and renew a right spirit with - in me.
Or: There is none but you to uphold our cause; our sin cries out and our guilt is great.
Or: Remember not the sins of my youth or my transgressions, but think on
me in your goodness, O Lord, according to your stead - fast love.

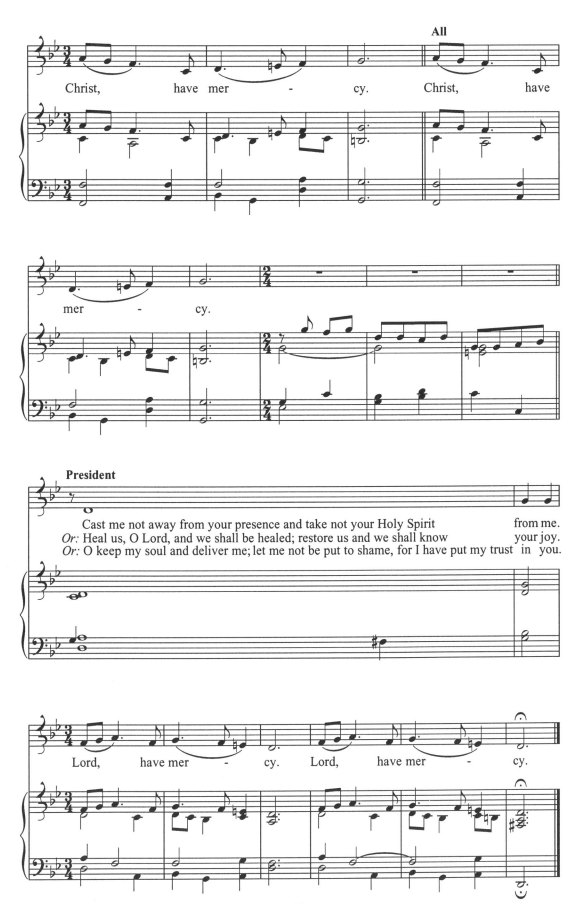

All

Christ, have mer - cy. Christ, have mer - cy.

President

Cast me not away from your presence and take not your Holy Spirit from me.
Or: Heal us, O Lord, and we shall be healed; restore us and we shall know your joy.
Or: O keep my soul and deliver me; let me not be put to shame, for I have put my trust in you.

Lord, have mer - cy. Lord, have mer - cy.

13

THE LITURGY OF THE WORD

Readings

Andrew Moore

This is the word of the Lord. Thanks be to God.

An acclamation may herald the Gospel Reading. See page next page for suitable settings.

Gospel Reading

Andrew Moore

Hear the Gos - pel of our Lord Je - sus Christ ac -

cord - ing to N. Glo - ry to you, O Lord.

At the end

Optional Descant

Praise to you, O Christ.

This is the Gos - pel of the Lord. Praise to you, O Christ.

Gospel Acclamations

Common Worship for the Celebration of Holy Communion introduces a Gospel Acclamation to be sung before the Gospel. Throughout the year, except from Ash Wednesday to Maundy Thursday, the form is as follows:

All	Alleluia
Cantor/Choir	sings a verse from scripture
All	Alleluia

From Ash Wednesday to Maundy Thursday the Alleluia is replaced by the response:
Praise to you, O Christ, King of eternal glory.

Below we give the texts for the Cantor/Choir, verse; musical settings will be found on pages 18-21. Any setting may be chosen for any text.

In the single and simple method of pointing the texts used, the move to the note after the reciting note is marked by the underlining of the syllable. So,

Speak, Lord, for your ser - <u>vant</u> is listening.   You have the words of e - <u>ter</u> - nal life.

Verses for Ordinary Time *(Turn to page 18 for musical settings)*

1
Speak, Lord, for your ser<u>vant</u> is listening.
You have the words of e<u>ter</u>nal life.   *1 Samuel 3.9; John 6.68*

2
I am the light of the world, <u>says</u> the Lord.
Whoever follows me will never walk in darkness
but will have the <u>light</u> of life.   *John 8.12*

3
My sheep hear my voice, <u>says</u> the Lord.
I know them, and they <u>foll</u>ow me.   *John 10.27*

4
I am the way, the truth, and the life, <u>says</u> the Lord.
No one comes to the Father ex<u>cept</u> through me.   *John 14.6*

5
We do not live by <u>bread</u> alone,
but by every word that comes from the <u>mouth</u> of God.   *Matthew 4.4*

6
Welcome with meekness the im<u>plant</u>ed word
that has the power to <u>save</u> your souls.   *James 1.21*

7
The word of the Lord en<u>dures</u> for ever.
The word of the Lord is the good news an<u>nounced</u> to you.   *cf 1 Peter 1.25*

Verses for the Seasons *(Turn to page 18-21 for musical settings)*

From the First Sunday of Advent until Christmas Eve
Prepare the way of the Lord, make his paths straight,
and all flesh shall see the salvation of God.   *cf Isaiah 40.3-5*

From Christmas Day until the Eve of the Epiphany
The Word became flesh and dwelt among us,
and we have seen his glory.   *John 1.14*

From the Epiphany until the Eve of the Presentation
Christ was revealed in flesh, proclaimed among the nations
and believed in throughout the world.   *cf 1 Timothy 3.16*

The Presentation of Christ in the Temple
This child is the light to enlighten the nations,
and the glory of your people Israel.   *cf Luke 2.32*

From Ash Wednesday until the Saturday after the Fourth Sunday of Lent
The Lord is a great God, O that today you would listen to his voice.
Harden not your hearts.   *cf Psalm 95.3,7-8*

The Annunciation of Our Lord
The Word became flesh and lived among us,
and we have seen his glory.   *John 1.14*

Note: if the Annunciation falls in Eastertide, use the text provided for Christmas.

From the Fifth Sunday of Lent until the Wednesday of Holy Week
Christ humbled himself and became obedient unto death,
even death on a cross.
Therefore God has highly exalted him
and given him the name that is above every name.   *Philippians 2.8-9*

Maundy Thursday
I give you a new commandment, says the Lord:
Love one another as I have loved you.   *cf John 13.34*

From Easter Day until the Eve of the Ascension
I am the first and the last, says the Lord, and the living one;
I was dead, and behold I am alive for evermore.   *cf Revelation 1.17-18*

Ascension Day
Go and make disciples of all nations, says the Lord.
Remember, I am with you always, to the end of the age.   *cf Matthew 28.19-20*

From the day after Ascension Day until the Day of Pentecost
Come, Holy Spirit, fill the hearts of your faithful people
and kindle in them the fire of your love.

Trinity Sunday
Glory to the Father, and to the Son, and to the Holy Spirit,
one God, who was, and who is, and who is to come, the Almighty.   *cf Revelation 1.8*

All Saints' Day

You are a chosen race, a royal priesthood,
a holy nation, God's own people,
called out of darkness into his marvellous light.

1 Peter 2.9

From the day after All Saints' Day until the day before the First Sunday of Advent

Blessed is the king who comes in the name of the Lord.
Peace in heaven and glory in the highest heaven.

Luke 19.38

On Saints' Days

I have called you friends, says the Lord,
for all that I have heard from my Father I have made known to you.

cf John 15.15

See pages 16-18 for the proper texts

Richard Lloyd

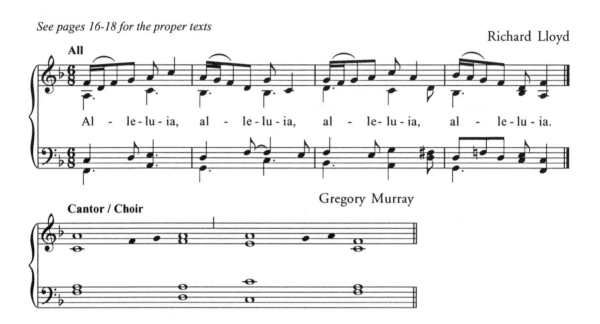

Gregory Murray

Unknown arr. John Ballantine

lu - jah! Hal - le - lu - jah, hal - le - lu - jah!

Gregory Murray

Gregory Murray

Cantor / Choir

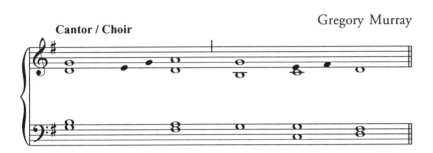

Malcolm Archer

All

Al - le - lu - ia, al - le - lu - ia, al - le - lu - ia, al - le - lu - ia,

al - le - lu - ia, al - le - lu - ia, al - le - lu - ia, al - le - lu - ia.

Gregory Murray

Cantor / Choir

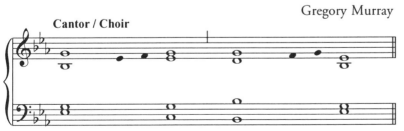

Plainsong arr. Andrew Moore

Al - le - lu - ia, al - le - lu - ia, al - le - lu - ia.

Gregory Murray

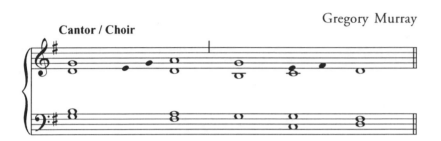

Fintan O'Carroll

Al - le - lu - ia, al - le - lu - ia,

Al - le - lu - ia, al - le - lu - ia.

Gregory Murray

Easter Alleluia

Plainsong arr. Andrew Moore

Al - le - lu - ia, al - le - lu - ia, al - le - lu - ia.

Cantor / Choir Gregory Murray

From Ash Wednesday to Maundy Thursday

Andrew Moore

Praise to you, O Christ, King of e - ter - nal glo - ry.

Praise to you, O Christ, King of e - ter - nal glo - ry!

Cantor / Choir Gregory Murray

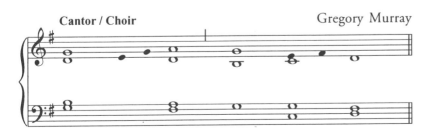

Prayers of Intercession

Lord, in your mer - cy hear our prayer.

OR

Lord, hear us. Lord, gra-cious-ly hear us.

OR

Hear us, good Lord. Lord, Lord, have mer - cy.

OR

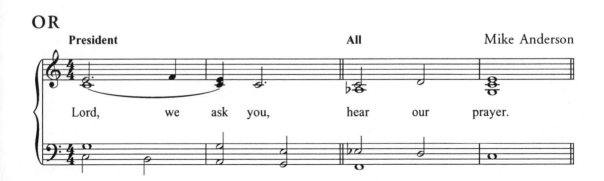

Lord, we ask you, hear our prayer.

At the end

Mer - ci - ful Fa - ther, ac - cept these prayers for the sake of your

Son, our Sa - viour Je - sus Christ. A - men.

THE LITURGY OF THE SACRAMENT

The Peace

Christopher Tambling

The peace of the Lord be al - ways with you and al-so with you.

Prayers at the Preparation of the Table

Rosalie Bonighton

Yours, Lord, is the greatness, the power, the glory, the splendour, and the majesty;

for everything in heaven and on earth is yours.

All things come from you, and of your own do we give you.

OR

Rosalie Bonighton

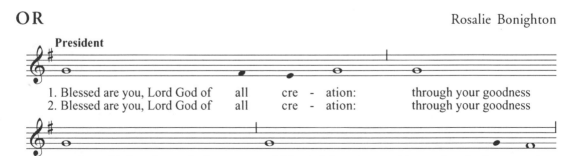

1. Blessed are you, Lord God of all cre - ation: through your goodness
2. Blessed are you, Lord God of all cre - ation: through your goodness

we have this bread to set before you, which earth has given and human hands have made.
we have this wine to set before you, fruit of the vine and work of hu - man hands.

All *(Harmony)*

It will become for us the bread of life.
It will become for us the cup of sal - vation.

Bles - sed be God for e - ver.

OR

Rosalie Bonighton

*President

With this bread that we bring

All *(Harmony)*

we shall re - mem - ber Je - sus.

President

With this wine that we bring

All *(Harmony)*

we shall re - mem - ber Je - sus.

President

Bread for his bo - dy, wine for his blood, gifts from God to his

poco rit.

ta - ble we bring.

All *(Harmony)*

a tempo

We shall re - mem - ber Je - sus.

* Or Cantor

Eucharistic Prayer A

David Terry

OR David Terry

OR David Terry

Christ has died: Christ is ris'n: Christ will come a - gain.

Dy - ing you des - troyed our death, ris - ing you res - tored our life: Lord Je - sus, come in glo - ry.

When we eat this bread and drink this cup, we pro - claim your death, Lord Je - sus, un - til you come in glo - ry.

David Terry

Eucharistic Prayer B

Settings for this Prayer will be found as follows:

Eucharistic Prayer C

Settings for this Prayer will be found as follows:

Eucharistic Prayer D

Christopher Tambling

The Lord be with you and al - so with you.

OR

Christopher Tambling

The Lord is here. His Spi - rit is with us.

Lift up your hearts. We lift them to the Lord.

Let us give thanks to the Lord our God.   It is right to give thanks and praise.

Almighty God, good Father to us all,   your face is turned to - wards your world.

In love you gave us Je-sus your Son to rescue us from sin and death.

Your Word goes out to call us home to the city where angels sing your praise.

All

We join with them in hea-ven's song: Ho - ly, ho - ly, ho - ly Lord,

God of pow-er and might, hea-ven and earth are full of your

glo - ry. Ho - san - na in the high - est. (Bles-sed is he who

comes in the name of the Lord. Ho - san - na in the high - est.)

President

Father of all, we give you thanks for every gift that comes from heaven.

To the darkness Jesus came as your light. With signs of faith and words of hope

he touched untoucha - bles with love and washed the guil - ty clean.

All *f*

This is his sto - ry. This is our song: Ho - san - na in the high - est.

President

The crowds came out to see your Son,

yet at the end they turned on him. On the night he was be - trayed

he came to table with his friends to celebrate the free - dom of your people.

All *f*

This is his sto - ry. This is our song: Ho - san - na in the high - est.

President

Jesus blessed you, Father, for the food; he took bread, gave thanks, broke it and said:

This is my body, gi - ven for you all. Jesus then gave thanks for the wine;

he took the cup, gave it and said: This is my blood, shed for you all

for the for - give - ness of sins. Do this in re - mem - brance of me.

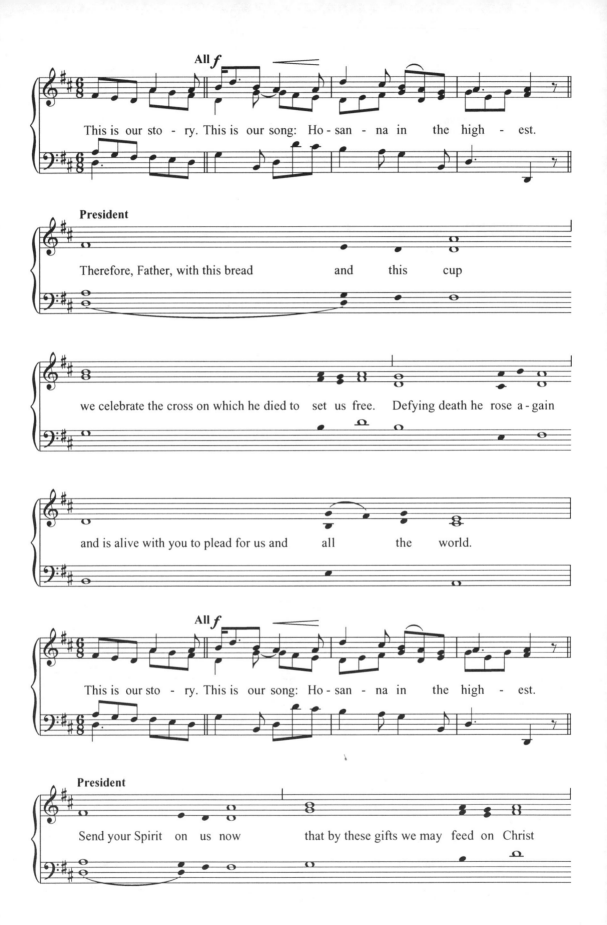

All _f_
This is our sto - ry. This is our song: Ho - san - na in the high - est.

President
Therefore, Father, with this bread and this cup

we celebrate the cross on which he died to set us free. Defying death he rose a - gain

and is alive with you to plead for us and all the world.

All _f_
This is our sto - ry. This is our song: Ho - san - na in the high - est.

President
Send your Spirit on us now that by these gifts we may feed on Christ

with opened eyes and hearts on fire.

May we and all who share this food offer ourselves to live for you

and be welcomed at your feast in heaven

where all cre - a - tion worships you, Father, Son and Ho - ly Spirit:

All *f*

Bles - sing and hon-our and glo - ry and pow-er be yours for e - ver and

e - ver. A - men.

Eucharistic Prayer E

Settings for this Prayer will be found as follows:

Eucharistic Prayer F

Alan Rees

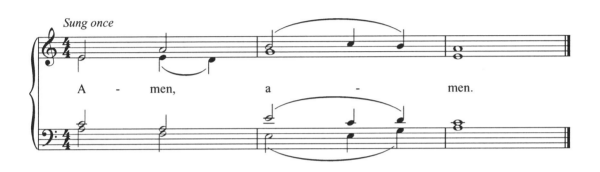

Eucharistic Prayer G

Settings for this Prayer will be found as follows:

Eucharistic Prayer H

Andrew Moore

President: The Lord be with you
All: and al-so with you.
Or: The Lord is here. His Spi-rit is with us.

President: Lift up your hearts.
All: We lift them to the Lord.

President: Let us give thanks to the Lord our God.
All: It is right to give him thanks and praise.

President: It is right to praise you, Father, Lord of all cre-ation; in your love you made us for your-self.

When we turned away you did not re-ject us, but came to meet us in your Son.

All: You em-braced us as your child-ren and wel-comed us to sit and eat with you.

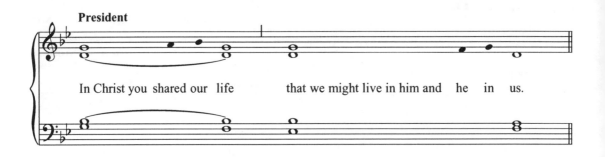

President

In Christ you shared our life that we might live in him and he in us.

All

He o - pened his arms of love up - on the cross and

made for all the per - fect sac - ri - fice for sin.

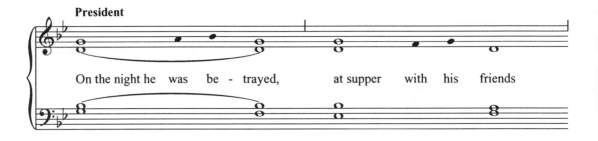

President

On the night he was be - trayed, at supper with his friends

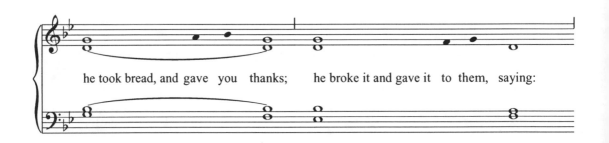

he took bread, and gave you thanks; he broke it and gave it to them, saying:

Slower

Take, eat; this is my body which is gi - ven for you; do this in re - mem - brance of me.

All

Fa - ther, we do this in re - mem - brance of

him: his bo - dy is the bread of life.

President

At the end of supper, taking the cup of wine, he gave you thanks, and said:

Slower

Drink this, all of you; this is the blood of the new co - ve - nant,

which is shed for you for the forgive -ness of sins; do this in re - mem - brance of me.

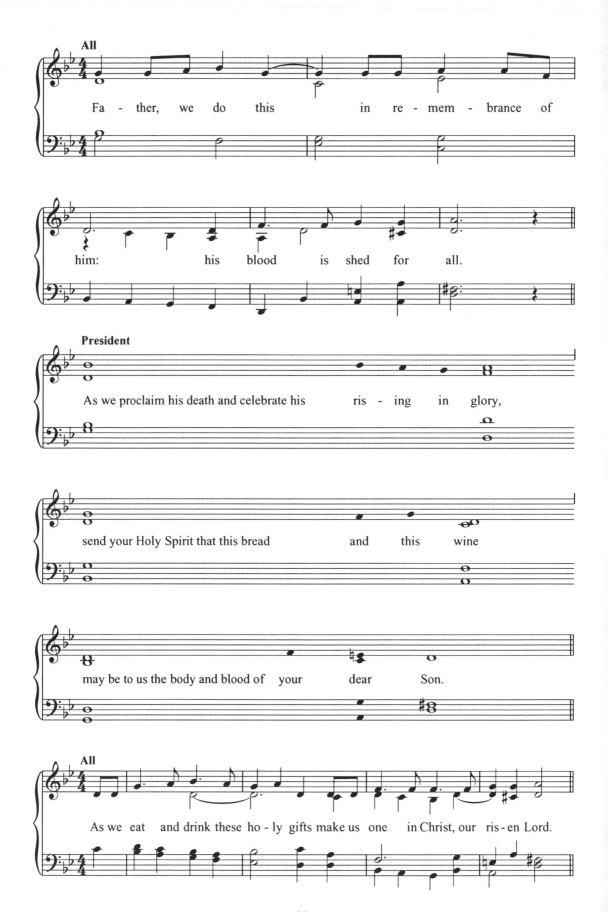

President

With your whole Church through-out the world we offer you this sacri-fice of

praise and lift our voice to join the e-ter-nal song of hea-ven:

All

Ho-ly, ho-ly, ho-ly Lord, God of pow-er and

God of might, hea-ven and earth are full of your glo-ry. Ho-

san-na in the high-est. Ho-san-na in the high-est. Ho-

san-na in the high-est. Ho-san-na in the high-est.

Additional Eucharistic Acclamations

David Hill

Christ has died: Christ is ri-sen: Christ will come a-gain.

Optional Descant
Christ has died: Christ is ri-sen: Christ will come a-gain.

Christ has died: Christ is ri-sen: Christ will come a-gain.

OR

Philip Duffy

Dy-ing you de-stroyed our death, ris-ing you re-stored our life: Lord Je-sus, come in glo-ry, Lord Je-sus, come in glo-ry.

OR

When we eat this bread and drink this cup, we pro - claim your

death, Lord Je - sus, un - til you come in

glo - ry, un - til you come in glo - ry.

Alan Rees

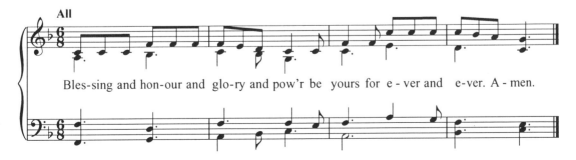

Bles-sing and hon-our and glo-ry and pow'r be yours for e - ver and e-ver. A - men.

O Sa - viour of the world,

who by thy cross and pre - cious blood hast re - deemed us,

save us, and help us, we hum - bly be - seech thee, O Lord.

Margaret Rizza

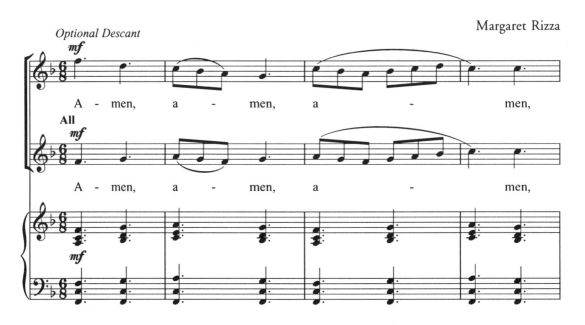

Optional Descant

A - men, a - men, a - men,

A - men, a - men, a - men,

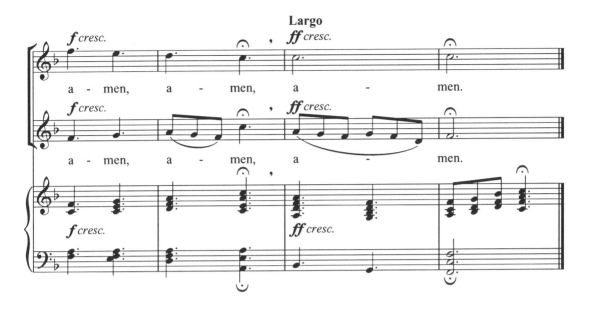

OR

David Hill

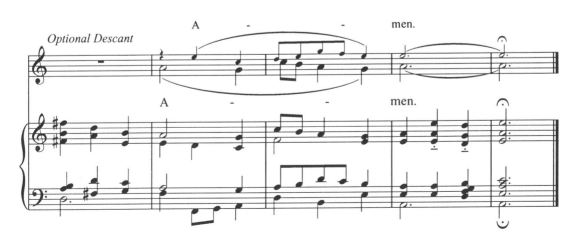

Plainsong arr. Andrew Moore

Alan Rees

Breaking of the Bread

Christopher Tambling

President

We break this bread to share in the bo - dy of Christ.

All

Though we are ma-ny, we are one bo-dy, be-cause we all share in one bread.

OR

Christopher Tambling

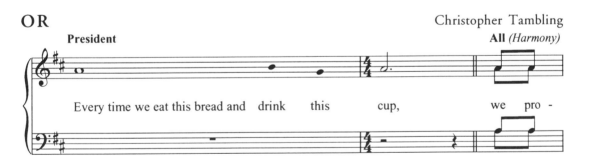

President

All *(Harmony)*

Every time we eat this bread and drink this cup, we pro -

claim the Lord's death un - til he comes.

Giving of Communion

David Terry

President

Jesus is the Lamb of God who takes away the sin of the world.

Blessed are those who are called to his supper.

All *mf*

Lord, I am not wor-thy to re-ceive you, but

on-ly say the word, and I shall be healed.

OR

David Terry

President

God's holy gifts for God's holy people.

Jesus Christ is holy, Jesus Christ is Lord, to the glory of God the Father.

OR

David Terry

Alleluia. Christ our passover is sacrificed for us. Therefore let us keep the feast. Alleluia.

OR
Traditional Language Setting

David Terry

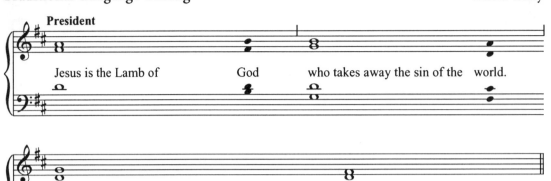

President

Jesus is the Lamb of God who takes away the sin of the world.

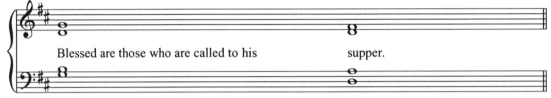

Blessed are those who are called to his supper.

All *mf*

Lord, I am not wor - thy that thou should-est come un-der my roof, but

speak the word on - ly and my soul shall be healed.

THE DISMISSAL

Malcolm Archer

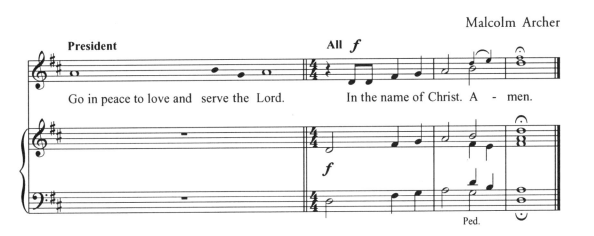

OR

Rosalie Bonighton

Optional Choral Part

Rosalie Bonighton

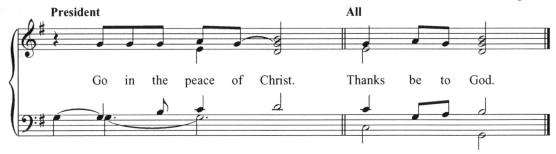

Go in the peace of Christ. Thanks be to God.

OR

From Easter Day to Pentecost

Rosalie Bonighton

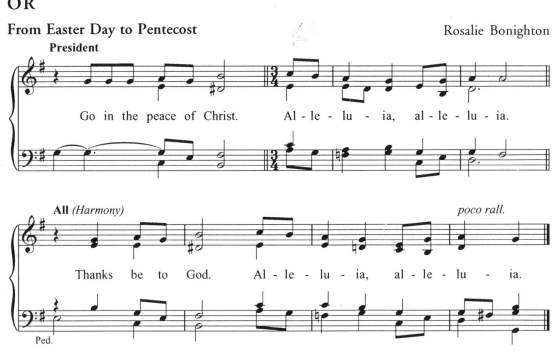

Go in the peace of Christ. Al - le - lu - ia, al - le - lu - ia.

Thanks be to God. Al - le - lu - ia, al - le - lu - ia.

Thanks be to God. Al - le - lu - ia, al - le - lu - ia.